Diary
2024 †

Through the Year with
Twelve Parables of Jesus

Fr Denis McBride C.Ss.R.

redemptorist
publications

Published by Redemptorist Publications
Chawton, Hampshire, GU34 3HQ, UK
Tel. +44 (0)1420 88222, Fax. +44 (0)1420 88805
Email rp@rpbooks.co.uk, www.rpbooks.co.uk

A registered charity limited by guarantee
Registered in England 03261721

Edited by Caroline Hodgson
Designed by Eliana Thompson

ISBN 978-0-85231-639-9

A CIP catalogue record for this book is available from
the British Library.

The publisher gratefully acknowledges permission to use
the following copyright material:

Cover image: *Parable of the Sower*, Stained glass window
from Canterbury Cathedral © Lawrence OP
Image for August: *Le Fils Prodigue* by Arcabas.

Excerpts from The Jerusalem Bible, copyright © 1966 by
Darton, Longman & Todd, Ltd and Doubleday, a division of
Random House, Inc. Reprinted by permission.

Excerpts from the New Revised Standard Version of the Bible:
Anglicised Edition, © 1989. 1995, Division of Christian
Education of the National Council of the Churches of Christ
in the United States of America. Used by permission.
All rights reserved.

Every effort has been made to trace copyright holders and
to obtain their permission for the use of copyright material.
The publisher apologises for any errors or omissions and
would be grateful for notification of any corrections that should
be incorporated in future reprints or editions of this book.

Printed by Short Run Press Ltd, Exeter

Personal Information

Name:

Address:

Telephone:

Mobile:

Email:

IN CASE OF AN EMERGENCY PLEASE INFORM

Name:

Telephone:

Mobile:

DOCTOR

Name:

Telephone:

Info:

Blood group:

Rh.

Name and Address

Telephone

Name and Address

Telephone

†Through the Year with
Twelve Parables of Jesus

Through the Year with
Twelve Parables of Jesus

Why tell stories?

All tribes and all peoples have a treasure of sacred stories. In many cultures it was the storyteller who introduced people to their own identity and their own history, giving them a sense of belonging to a larger story than their own. These stories have the function of establishing a narrative beginning to creation / nation / tribe and preserving a particular way of seeing the world. The stories were told in the belief that people's identities seem largely determined by the kind of story they believe they inhabit. Without those stories there is a sense of alienation not only from what has happened before but from what is happening within. Without stories there is little opportunity to discover a way of seeing the world or a way of seeing ourselves.

We can tell stories for all sorts of reasons:

> to establish who we are and where we came from;
> to preserve our traditions, to defend our way of seeing things;
> to tell lies and hide painful truths;
> to pass the time, to entertain, to enlighten;
> to expose oppressive behaviour and hypocrisy;
> to question cherished myths, to introduce new thinking.

The appeal to narrative as a way of understanding the world and oneself is not based simply on an interest in story nor in recognition of the story's privileged place in the Jewish and Christian traditions. As Michael Goldberg points out: "Instead, it is the much stronger view that virtually all our convictions, nonreligious as well as religious, are rooted in some narrative, and that frequently, our most serious disputes with one another reflect rival narrative accounts."[1]

A particular community's sacred stories give shape to its sense of identity; they provide a setting for belief; they give rise to convictions and claims which are later abstracted from the original narrative and placed in a dogmatic framework. A community's sacred stories, however, may provoke profound disagreement among those who do not belong to that community or among its

---

1   M. Goldberg, *Theology and Narrative: a critical introduction*
     (Nashville: Abingdon, 1982), 36.

own members who can no longer subscribe to the stories' claims. Stories told, for instance, to uphold the supremacy of a particular race or justify entitlement to a particular land are rarely tales without victims – which is why counter stories are formed to question that particular way of looking at the world.

The power of fiction

Parables, of course, are fictional stories: their claim to truth does not pretend to be based on historical reminiscence or real events. When we hear or read a story we know to be a work of fiction, our first reaction may be to think of it simply as entertainment: "Interesting, yes, but it's only a story after all." Knowing a story to be fictional might lead us to dismiss any claims the story might make on us. Some people believe that historical narrative or reportage is the only "real story" worthy of their attention.

A rabbi teacher of mine told me how he found it more difficult to tell stories to Gentiles than to Jews. When you tell a story to a Gentile, he said, you hear two recurring questions: Is it true? Did it really happen?

He answers the first question by saying, "Yes, it is true." And the second by saying, "No, it didn't really happen." He said that when he tells his Jewish congregation a story, their question is: What does it mean?

Elie Wiesel eloquently makes the same point when he tells the story of meeting a rabbi friend of his grandfather's in Tel Aviv, after an interim of twenty years, and tries to explain what he is doing with his life:

> "Tell me what you are doing," the Rebbe said in a soft voice. I told him I was writing. "Is that all?" he asked in disbelief. I said yes, that's all. His expression was so reproachful that I had to elaborate and explain that some writings could sometimes, in moments of grace, attain the quality of deeds. He did not seem to understand…
> "What are you writing?" the Rebbe asked. "Stories," I said. He wanted to know what kind of stories: true stories. "About

people you knew?" Yes, about people I might have known. "About things that happened?" Yes, about things that happened or could have happened. "But they did not?" No, not all of them did. In fact some were invented from almost the beginning to almost the end. The Rebbe leaned forward as if to measure me up and said with more sorrow than anger: "That means you are writing lies!" I did not answer immediately. The scolded child within me had nothing to say in his defence. Yet, I had to justify myself: "Things are not that simple, Rebbe. Some events do take place but are not true; others are - although they never occurred."[2]

Wiesel saw himself as an inheritor of a rich biblical tradition where writers have always felt free to use a variety of resources from the literary store cupboard: oral tradition, ancestral myths, legends, folk-tales, dreams, visions, tribal customs, parables, hymns, genealogies, doxologies, testimonials, prayers, etc. All these were pressed into service to communicate the truth of their message. To confine the biblical writers to answering one concern – "Just tell us what actually happened!" – would not only be anachronistic but subscribe to the curious belief that all people really need in order to change is accurate information. Luke caricatured this naïve belief in the parable of the Rich Man and Lazarus, when Abraham says: "If they do not listen to Moses and the prophets, neither will they be convinced even if someone rises from the dead" (Luke 16:31).

How do you challenge people to change?
Throughout the Synoptic Gospels the evangelists show us Jesus inviting his hearers to use their imagination and travel into the world of parable. Sympathetic imagination enables us as listeners or readers to cross the bridge between where we are and where others are, between the way we see things and different ways of seeing the same things. While it is difficult to recover the original historical setting that gave rise to any particular parable spoken by Jesus – many of the parables are contained within blocks of teaching by the evangelists (e.g., Mark 4:1-34; Mattew 24:32 - 25:46) – the nature of the parable form will help us in our task.

---

2   E. Wiesel, *Legends of our Time* (New York: Avon Books, 1970), viii.

As J. Jeremias notes: "They [the parables] were mostly concerned with a situation of conflict – with justification, defence, attack, and even challenge. For the most part, though not exclusively, they are weapons of controversy. Every one of them calls for an answer on the spot."[3]

The parables are challenges to change. They are a way of confronting people. Through the parables the evangelists present us with a Jesus who invites his hearers to use their imagination to focus on vulnerable groups or oppressive attitudes in the hope that they will see things differently.

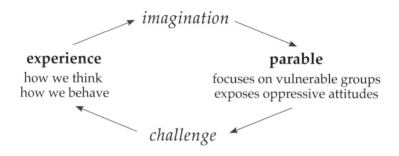

imagination

experience
how we think
how we behave

parable
focuses on vulnerable groups
exposes oppressive attitudes

challenge

Challenging people to think differently, however, is a risky pastime – not least because most of us want to be left alone to nourish our cherished prejudices. If few of us welcome criticism, fewer have a gift for offering it. How do you confront people who see things differently? How do you challenge a friend who is involved in destructive behaviour? How do you tell people things you know they do not want to hear? Answers to these questions depend largely on our cultural background and personality, but most attempts at confronting others follow either the direct approach, which concentrates on naming the problem, or the indirect approach, which has the dual focus of the problem and the relationship between the two parties.

---

3 J. Jeremias, *The Parables of Jesus* (London: SCM, 1972), 21.

a) **Direct confrontation** In this way you confront others directly by going straight to the point; you "tell it like it is". There is no attempt to disguise the issue, no striving after diplomatic language, no "beating around the bush". Your strategy is to name unambiguously what concerns you about the thinking or behaviour of the offending party. The speakers often call this "constructive criticism"; rarely is it so perceived by the listeners, who may feel affronted by what they hear. Sometimes direct confrontation accomplishes little because, no matter how accurate the criticism, it is registered by the hearers as destructive, so that they end up feeling disabled. What they hear might only serve to confirm a larger script that others have written about them: that they are born losers, that they can get nothing right, that they are chronic failures. If the only time we relate to people is when we confront them and give them a piece of our mind, in all probability the confrontation will not have the desired result. It is difficult to challenge people profitably if there is no supporting relationship to sustain the criticism.

b) **Indirect confrontation** In some cultures direct confrontation is regarded as crude and harmful to relationships; instead, the confrontation is done indirectly through the medium of go-betweens or by using indirect language. This method tries to avoid anything that looks like antagonism, using coded language that needs interpretation. Although the indirect method seeks to face the issue, there is the added focus on the relationship between the parties. The reason the confrontation is managed indirectly is because of the underlying concern that the relationship should not be irreparably damaged in the process of "telling the truth".

Conflict and contrast

All stories progress by way of conflict; while some conclude with resolution, others are deliberately left open-ended. "Once upon a time everyone lived happily ever after" is not a story, but the absence of story. If you watch a film or read a novel, the opening format is predictably the same as ancient storytelling: something goes wrong quickly. This establishes the plot and immediately introduces a series of questions. How are people going to react in this situation? How are they going to relate to one another? How is the problem going to be solved? Hence the immediate conflict in the parables: a shepherd loses a sheep; a housewife loses a coin; people invited to a banquet refuse to turn up; a widow is refused justice; a friend arrives unannounced, etc. These problems arouse our interest in the brief ensuing drama.

Storytelling also needs contrast and variety; it needs difference if the story is to proceed. So in the parables you find the contrast between virtue and vice, wisdom and stupidity, graciousness and meanness, poverty and plenty. In the stories of Jesus we are invited to enter a visual world of dinner parties, sheepfolds, vineyards, welcome households, dangerous journeys. It is a world of great variety. You meet all sorts of people: difficult judges, committed burglars, broken families, wounded beggars, awkward neighbours, selfish priests, eccentric employers, desperate hosts, surprised guests, wise and foolish virgins.

You see how differently people act and react: with generosity, with fear, with delight, with suspicion, with jealousy, with energy, with open arms, with closed hearts. We are invited not only to think but also to feel, to find ourselves somewhere inside the story, to be questioned by the issues it raises.

The invitation to think anew

If the parables work, they leave us wondering not just about the dynamics of an interesting story but about deeply personal and social questions we face every day. Parables are not fictional diversions from real life but deliberate probes into the lives we actually live. They call us to think again about how we see and how we behave, to think again about attitudes and behaviour in our community or society that we accept lazily or uncritically. The parables of Jesus *make the ordinary important*: Jesus speaks out of a theology of ordinariness when he begins his theological thinking with things as they are. Religion is not primarily about special cultic activities or secret wisdom; it is about loving the God who created us and loving the neighbour we find ourselves beside. Liturgy can be left to one side when more important business, like forgiving our brother or sister, is waiting as the real religious agenda.

In Jesus' parables there is a marked absence of the supernatural. Jesus baptises the ordinary and tells us that it is in the theatre of the ordinary that the drama of salvation is being lived out. By calling on everyday experience, the parables tell us that we are saved where we are. Salvation is primarily something that happens to people in the midst of life. The word that Jesus often puts beside salvation is "Today". Thus he meets the cautious repentance of Zacchaeus with the generous word of Gospel: "Today salvation has come to this house" (Luke 19:9).

In the parables we are invited to make a choice and come to a decision; we are commanded to pay attention and face issues we might prefer to ignore. The parables tell us that it is in the midst of the everyday – the regular, mundane business of our eating, drinking, sleeping, choosing, loving, forgiving, reaching out, journeying, noticing people, answering doors, offering hospitality, sharing bread, and listening to midnight stories - that our happiness and salvation are being worked out. Through the parables we learn that inside the story of our everyday life lies the deeper story of our salvation.

Denis McBride cssr

Fr Denis McBride, C.Ss.R.
Publishing Director

	January	February	March	April	May	June
Mon	1			1		
Tue	2			2		
Wed	3			3	1	
Thu	4	1		4	2	
Fri	5	2	1	5	3	
Sat	6	3	2	6	4	1
Sun	7	4	3	7	5	2
Mon	8	5	4	8	6	3
Tue	9	6	5	9	7	4
Wed	10	7	6	10	8	5
Thu	11	8	7	11	9	6
Fri	12	9	8	12	10	7
Sat	13	10	9	13	11	8
Sun	14	11	10	14	12	9
Mon	15	12	11	15	13	10
Tue	16	13	12	16	14	11
Wed	17	14	13	17	15	12
Thu	18	15	14	18	16	13
Fri	19	16	15	19	17	14
Sat	20	17	16	20	18	15
Sun	21	18	17	21	19	16
Mon	22	19	18	22	20	17
Tue	23	20	19	23	21	18
Wed	24	21	20	24	22	19
Thu	25	22	21	25	23	20
Fri	26	23	22	26	24	21
Sat	27	24	23	27	25	22
Sun	28	25	24	28	26	23
Mon	29	26	25	29	27	24
Tue	30	27	26	30	28	25
Wed	31	28	27		29	26
Thu		29	28		30	27
Fri			29		31	28
Sat			30			29
Sun			31			30
Mon						
Tue						

July	August	September	October	November	December	
1						Mon
2			1			Tue
3			2			Wed
4	1		3			Thu
5	2		4	1		Fri
6	3		5	2		Sat
7	4	1	6	3	1	Sun
8	5	2	7	4	2	Mon
9	6	3	8	5	3	Tue
10	7	4	9	6	4	Wed
11	8	5	10	7	5	Thu
12	9	6	11	8	6	Fri
13	10	7	12	9	7	Sat
14	11	8	13	10	8	Sun
15	12	9	14	11	9	Mon
16	13	10	15	12	10	Tue
17	14	11	16	13	11	Wed
18	15	12	17	14	12	Thu
19	16	13	18	15	13	Fri
20	17	14	19	16	14	Sat
21	18	15	20	17	15	Sun
22	19	16	21	18	16	Mon
23	20	17	22	19	17	Tue
24	21	18	23	20	18	Wed
25	22	19	24	21	19	Thu
26	23	20	25	22	20	Fri
27	24	21	26	23	21	Sat
28	25	22	27	24	22	Sun
29	26	23	28	25	23	Mon
30	27	24	29	26	24	Tue
31	28	25	30	27	25	Wed
	29	26	31	28	26	Thu
	30	27		29	27	Fri
	31	28		30	28	Sat
		29			29	Sun
		30			30	Mon
					31	Tue

December 2023/January 2024

Sunday *The Holy Family of Jesus, Mary & Joseph*

31

Monday *Mary, the Holy Mother of God*

1 *New Year's Bank Holiday*

Tuesday *Ss Basil & Gregory*

2

Wednesday

3

✝

January

Thursday
4

Friday
5

Saturday *The Epiphany of the Lord* (Ireland)
6

The Parable of the Last Judgement

Matthew 25:31-46

*I*n the apocalyptic vision of the Last Judgement, given to the disciples prior to his death, Jesus focuses attention on his continuing presence among the needy. It is as if Jesus deliberately turns his own followers away from an exclusive attraction to himself, away from a restricted focus on his own person, to look elsewhere to find him. In so doing, he challenges us to face the pain and loss endured by others, not keep staring at him. He will be found where others suffer.

The only division made is between those who connected with needy people and those who remained disconnected from them. People are welcomed as "blessed by my Father" because they have paid attention not to the Father or the Son but to the legion of the vulnerable within their reach. Six categories of people in distress are listed, together with six appropriate responses.

Those who are vulnerable	Those who pay attention
the hungry	give food
the thirsty	give drink
"I" the stranger	"You" offer welcome
the naked	clothe
the sick	visit
the imprisoned	go to see

In the left-hand column there is a list of vulnerable human beings whose needs await recognition and practical help, together with the startling revelation that Jesus' presence abides among them. In the right-hand column there is a list of humane responses by the just, together with the startling revelation that Jesus himself was the beneficiary of these acts of kindness. The blessed are commended for their actions, not their attitudes; for what they did, not for what they thought. Misery obliged them to act, so their active verbs prove to be what is important. Their response was humane and, therefore, profoundly religious; it is hallowed as the kingdom response of those who take responsibility for a broken world.

In his reflections on humanity, the distinguished Jewish philosopher Abraham Heschel makes a distinction between *human being* and *being human*: while we are all human beings, being human is something we become or fail to become. Humanity is not a given but a goal for every human being. He writes: "The degree to which one is sensitive to other people's suffering, to other men's humanity, is the index of one's own humanity. It is the root not only for social living but for the study of humanities… The central problem of biblical thinking is not: 'What is *to be*?' but rather: 'How to be and how not to be?'"[1] That, it seems to me, is the question of the Last Judgement.

Edward Burne-Jones, *The Last Judgement, detail*, 1897

1   A. J. Heschel, *Who is Man?* (California: Stanford University Press, 1975), 46-47.

January

Sunday *The Epiphany of the Lord (E&W,S)*
7 *The Baptism of the Lord (Ireland)*

Monday 1st Week in Ordinary Time
8 *The Baptism of the Lord (E&W,S)*

Tuesday
9

Wednesday
10

✝

Thursday
11

Friday
12

Saturday *St Kentigern (Scotland)*
13

I was hungry and you gave me food,
I was thirsty and you gave me something to drink,
I was a stranger and you welcomed me,
I was naked and you gave me clothing,
I was sick and you took care of me,
I was in prison and you visited me.

Matthew 25:35-36

January

Sunday *2nd Sunday in Ordinary Time*

14 *Peace Day (E&W)*

Monday

15

Tuesday

16

Wednesday *St Anthony, Abbot*

17

✝

January

Thursday *Octave of Prayer for Christian Unity (18-25 January)*
18

Friday
19

Saturday
20

January

Sunday *3rd Sunday in Ordinary Time*

21 *Sunday of the Word of God*

Monday

22

Tuesday

23

Wednesday *St Francis de Sales*

24

Thursday *The Conversion of St Paul the Apostle*

25

Friday *Ss Timothy & Titus*

26

Saturday

27

January

Sunday
28
4th Sunday in Ordinary Time
Racial Justice Day (E&W)

Monday
29

Tuesday
30

Wednesday
31
St John Bosco

✝

February

Thursday St Brigid
1

Friday The Presentation of the Lord
2

Saturday
3

The Parable of the Great Banquet

Luke 14:16-24

*I*f you organise a party for your friends, you naturally invite those whose company you enjoy and want to share, the people who will provide the mixture of magic and agreeable contrast needed for a good party. But what happens when, after expressing their ready support for the idea, all your guests decide that they have better things to do and turn you down?

What happens when people react with studied indifference to all the preparations you have made, to say nothing about how you might feel? How do you respond to their choice not to come? How do you face the rejection that you inevitably feel in the face of such a public refusal?

In Luke's parable, the host declines to retire inside his own hurt and rejection; instead, he chooses again, moves out again, risks in a new way. Rather than providing a sad ending to the story, the rejection moves the narrative on, precisely because of the host's response. Confronted with an empty room and a banquet prepared, he stays fixed on his plan for feasting. When the chosen say no, there is a new urgency to ensure that the feast is enjoyed by others, which means that the host must choose again if he wants to fulfil his express desire "that my house may be filled." The feast is still on, but the faces are different around the table.

Given that the host wants the feast to be celebrated, the experience of rejection by the people he has chosen forces him to become more catholic in his choice of dinner companions. By force of circumstance he has to look for companionship where he normally never looks – beyond the circle of his cronies and friends to the legion of the overlooked. Rejection leads him to share table fellowship with people he would otherwise never have met.

Pieter Bruegel the Elder, Peasant Wedding

In all this there is a stubborn refusal to be disabled by rejection alongside an equally stubborn commitment to keep the show on the road. Jesus continues to extend his message of good news and his ministry of table fellowship to those beyond the boundaries of social and religious approval. Jesus feasts with toll collectors and sinners in the belief that *feasting together* provides an opportunity to bring salvation to people. The parable of the Great Banquet celebrates the movement of Jesus' mission ever outwards, one that his followers will extend farther in opening up table fellowship to the Gentiles.

February

Sunday *5th Sunday in Ordinary Time*

4

Monday *St Agatha*

5

Tuesday *St Paul Miki & Companions*

6

Wednesday

7

✝

February

Thursday _Day for Victims of Trafficking_

8

Friday

9

Saturday _St Scholastica_

10

Then the master said to the slave, "Go out into the roads and lanes, and compel people to come in, so that my house may be filled."

Luke 14:23

February

Sunday *6th Sunday in Ordinary Time*

11 *World Day for the Sick*

Day for the Unemployed (E&W)

Monday

12

Tuesday

13

Wednesday *Ash Wednesday*

14 *Ss Cyril & Methodius (Europe)*

St Valentine

✝

February

Thursday
15

Friday
16

Saturday
17

February

Sunday *1st Sunday of Lent*
18

Monday
19

Tuesday
20

Wednesday
21

✝

Thursday *The Chair of St Peter, Apostle*
22

Friday *Lent Fast Day*
23 *St Polycarp*

Saturday
24

February

Sunday *2nd Sunday of Lent*
25

Monday
26

Tuesday
27

Wednesday
28

✝

Thursday
29

Friday
1   Women's World Day of Prayer
       St David (Wales)

Saturday
2

A feast not shared

The parable of the Rich Man and Lazarus

Luke 14:16-24

*T*his parable offers us a counter image to the parable of the Great Banquet, serving to illustrate what the messianic banquet is *not* – feasting apart from the afflicted. In this story there is no invitation, no mention of guests, no host anxious to share his table, no surprised banqueters. A rich man feasts inside his house while outside, at his gate, a beggar lies wanting and waiting.

The opening of the parable paints the difference in summary strokes. The rich man is clothed in purple, a very expensive dye from the shellfish murex, used only by royalty and the elite governing classes. He feasts as he dresses, sumptuously, and his feasting is a daily commitment rather than an exceptional event.

In sharp contrast, at the gate of the rich man's house, lies Lazarus, one of society's expendables. His wardrobe is hardly magnificent – he is covered in sores – and he receives only the unwanted attention of street dogs that feed off his ulcerated sores. His hopes are humble, longing as he does not to eat at the rich man's table but only to feed off the scraps from the dinner table that were fed to the dogs. Lazarus hopes for what he has become: dog food. He waits.

After reporting the huge social gulf that exists between these two men, the first act concludes with reports on their deaths. When Lazarus dies, angels carry him to the bosom of Abraham; when the rich man dies, he receives a proper burial. The image of Abraham's bosom is clear: Lazarus is the honoured guest at the banquet of the patriarchs. *In the afterlife he is welcomed to a table fellowship he was so consistently denied in life.*

The rich man is now in agony, and the flames that surround him represent the destruction of everything he valued. His fine clothes are gone, his feasting is finished, his fate is fixed. He now becomes the beggar, pleading for mercy for himself and his brothers. In naming Lazarus, in expecting Lazarus to do his bidding, the rich man tells us that Lazarus was not one of the invisible poor, but known to him.

James Tissot, The Poor Lazarus at the Rich Man's Door

By refusing the rich man's requests, Abraham brings the focus back to everyday life, where the rich live unaffected by the plight of people who are poor and destitute. That is where the parable began, with the indefensible practice of a rich man feasting daily while a poor man lies destitute at his gate.

The message of the parable is clear: if the rich cannot *feast together* with the poor in this life, the poor shall feast without them in the kingdom.

March

Sunday *3rd Sunday of Lent*

3

Monday

4

Tuesday

5

Wednesday

6

✝

Thursday *Ss Perpetua & Felicity*
7

Friday *St John of God*
8

Saturday
9

There was a rich man who was dressed in purple and fine linen and who feasted sumptuously every day. And at his gate lay a poor man named Lazarus, covered with sores, who longed to satisfy his hunger with what fell from the rich man's table; even the dogs would come and lick his sores.

Luke 16:19-21

March

Sunday *4th Sunday of Lent*

10

Monday

11

Tuesday *Dementia Prayer Week 12-19th March*

12

Wednesday

13

✝

Thursday

14

Friday   *St Clement Hofbauer C.Ss.R.*

15

Saturday

16

March

Sunday
17
5th Sunday of Lent
St Patrick (Ireland)

Monday Bank Holiday (Ireland)
18

Tuesday *St Joseph, Spouse of the Blessed Virgin Mary*
19

Wednesday *St Cuthbert*
20

✝

Thursday
21

Friday
22

Saturday
23

March

Sunday *Palm Sunday of the Passion of the Lord*
24

Monday *Monday of Holy Week*
25

Tuesday *Tuesday of Holy Week*
26

Wednesday *Wednesday of Holy Week*
27

Thursday *Thursday of the Lord's Supper* (**Maundy Thursday**)

28

Friday *Friday of the Passion of the Lord* (**Good Friday**)

29 Bank Holiday

Saturday *Holy Saturday*

30

March/April

Sunday *Easter Sunday of the Resurrection of the Lord*

31 *Daylight Savings Time (BST) Begins*

Monday *Easter Monday*

1 *Bank Holiday*

Tuesday *Easter Tuesday*

2

Wednesday *Easter Wednesday*

3

Thursday Easter Thursday
4

Friday Easter Friday
5

Saturday Easter Saturday
6

✝

The Parable of the Sower

Matthew 13:1-9. 18-23

*A*farmer, desperate for a response, goes out into the fields and, with throwaway style, tosses the seed everywhere in the mad hope that somewhere the seed will take. The seed falls on the path, on rocky ground, among thorns, and some on good soil, resulting in a mixed harvest.

In the interpretation a variety of responses to the word of God is explored through four types of hearers. Firstly, there are those who hear the word without understanding it, and the word is easily taken from them by those who oppose its power. Secondly, there are those whose first enthusiasm for the word cannot withstand trial because the word has never taken root in them. Thirdly, there are those who hear the word but are overcome by a litany of distractions and lose it. Finally, there are those who hear the word and understand it, taking it to heart and making it their own, thus yielding a harvest through their persistence.

Underlying the parable there is a telling confidence: in spite of all the obstacles present in the various types of soil, the good news is that the seed does succeed in growing and producing a rich harvest. Today the word of God is still scattered generously, with throwaway style. God still risks the word, hoping that people will take to it, welcome it and make it their own. How would we describe our own responses to the word? Does it take root in us? Do we make serious efforts to understand it and know what it's asking of us? Do we welcome it with great show and then go our own sweet way anyway? Do we hear it and then smother it with our own concerns? Only we can answer the questions when we allow the parable to question us.

Vincent Van Gogh, The Sower

But we should be patient with ourselves. Like all seeds, the word of God takes time to grow. The sower knows that he has to wait for the weather, the secret workings of the soil, the slow thrust of life, before he can see the crops emerge. The sower cannot deny the time the whole process takes. God who sows the seed knows what it means to plant God's word in different people in different situations. It all takes time. But if we take the time to nourish the word, God will wait on the gradual process. It might take us a lifetime. But if we allow the seed to struggle to grow in us, we will grow too. Eventually the word of God and our own word might become one, making for a rich harvest.

April

Sunday *2nd Sunday of Easter*

7

Monday *The Annunciation of the Lord*

8

Tuesday

9

Wednesday

10

✝

Thursday
11

Friday
12

Saturday
13

B ut as for what was sown on good soil, this is the one who hears the word and understands it, who indeed bears fruit and yields, in one case a hundredfold, in another sixty, and in another thirty.

Matthew 13:23

April

Sunday *3rd Sunday of Easter*
14

Monday
15

Tuesday
16

Wednesday
17

✝

Thursday
18

Friday
19

Saturday
20

April

Sunday *4th Sunday of Easter*

21 *World Day of Prayer for Vocations*

Monday

22

Tuesday *St George (England)*

23

Wednesday

24

✝

Thursday *St Mark, Evangelist*
25

Friday
26

Saturday
27

April/May

Sunday   5th Sunday of Easter
28

Monday   St Catherine of Siena (Europe)
29

Tuesday   Day of Prayer for Survivors of Sexual Abuse
30

Wednesday   St Joseph the Worker
1

✝

Thursday St Athanasius

2

Friday Ss Philip & James, Apostles

3

Saturday

4

A Gospel for latecomers

The Parable of the Labourers in the Vineyard

Matthew 20:1-16

*T*he world of the Gospel is peopled with life's latecomers, who find themselves with some form of disability. They are the physically damaged, the psychologically damaged, the spiritually damaged, the economically damaged. They are the prodigal sons, the outcasts, the overlooked, the ones people think they can safely ignore or shun. They are found in the midst of the Gospel because they are in the midst of life. Jesus has a clear prejudice in their favour, not least because he teaches us what we keep unlearning: that God's ways are not our ways; that God does not work from the arithmetic of the calculator but from the fullness of a divine heart.

In today's Gospel Jesus gives us a marvellous insight into the wisdom of reversal which is at the heart of the kingdom. A landowner goes to the marketplace at dawn to hire casual labour to work in his vineyard. He arranges to pay them the average daily wage, one denarius. The landowner hires other labourers at nine in the morning, noon and mid-afternoon. About five o'clock, an hour before work ends at sunset, he hires the last group of workers. At six o'clock the fun starts: the first to be paid are the last to arrive, and they are given a full day's wage. Those who worked from dawn to sunset receive no more than those who put in only an hour's work in the cool of the evening. The landowner's generosity to the latecomers aggrieves the early starters, even though they are paid the agreed sum. So the landowner confronts them with the question: "Am I not allowed to do what I choose with what belongs to me? Or are you envious because I am generous?"

"Paytime", a Byzantine Gospel from the eleventh century

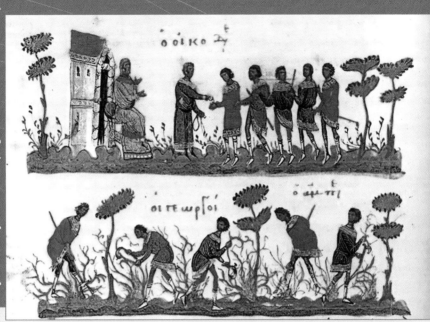

Do we allow God the freedom to do things the divine way, or do we get furious when God diverts from our way of operating? We may think it our right alone to sing "I did it my way", but what happens when we hear the Lord singing it? If we resent God's freedom to show mercy to whom God pleases, not only do we repeat the grumble of the labourers in the parable, but we forget how we ourselves benefit from God's mercy. As Shakespeare noted in *The Merchant of Venice*:

> Though justice be thy plea, consider this,
> That, in the course of justice, none of us
> Should see salvation: we do pray for mercy;
> And that same prayer doth teach us all to render
> The deeds of mercy.

May

Sunday *6th Sunday of Easter*

5

Monday *Early May Bank Holiday*

6

Tuesday

7

Wednesday

8

✝

May

Thursday *The Ascension of the Lord (E&W,S)*

9

Friday

10

Saturday

11

I choose to give to this last the same as I give to you. Am I not allowed to do what I choose with what belongs to me? Or are you envious because I am generous?

Matthew 20:14-15

May

Sunday *7th Sunday of Easter*
12
The Ascension of the Lord (Ireland)
World Communications Day (E&W,S)

Monday
13

Tuesday *St Matthias, Apostle*
14

Wednesday
15

Thursday
16

Friday
17

Saturday
18

May

Sunday *Pentecost Sunday*

19

Monday *7th Week in Ordinary Time*

20 *Blessed Virgin Mary, Mother of the Church*

Tuesday

21

Wednesday

22

Thursday *Our Lord Jesus Christ, the Eternal High Priest* (E&W)
23

Friday
24

Saturday *St Bede the Venerable (England)*
25

May

Sunday *The Most Holy Trinity*

26

Monday *8th Week in Ordinary Time*

27
Spring Bank Holiday
St Augustine of Canterbury (England)

Tuesday

28

Wednesday

29

Thursday

30

Friday *The Visitation of the Blessed Virgin Mary*

31

Saturday St Justin

1

The Parable of the Unforgiving Slave

Matthew 18:23-45

*T*he context for this parable is Matthew's concern to deal with relations between Christians, focusing on the need for forgiveness between members of the community. Peter asks Jesus how often he should forgive his brother, then answers his own question by suggesting seven times. The Jewish tradition taught that God forgives three times and punishes on the fourth occasion; it was not believed that injured people could be more gracious than God, so forgiveness was limited to three times. According to that tradition Peter's measure is generous; but according to Jesus it is radically insufficient. In his reply Jesus reverses the old law of vengeance: "If Cain is avenged sevenfold, truly Lamech seventy-sevenfold" (Genesis 4:24). Just as in the old days there was no limit to hatred and vengeance, so among Christians there is to be no limit to mercy and forgiveness.

The parable of the Unforgiving Slave is told in order to underline the need for forgiveness. When a king calls his court officials to audit the accounts, one shows a deficiency of ten thousand talents, a colossal sum of money. The sum is deliberately extravagant, running into millions of pounds, to heighten the contrast with the few pounds owed to the official. When the king orders the sale of the debtor and his family into slavery, the official pleads for time. The king feels sorry for him and decides to remit the whole of the vast debt. The official, however, learns nothing from his experience, for he refuses to give a colleague time to pay a trifling debt; instead, he has him thrown into prison. When this heartless behaviour is reported to the king, the grant of full forgiveness is retracted and the unforgiving official is thrown to the torturers.

Claude Vignon, Parable of the Unforgiving Servant

Apart from anything else, the unforgiving official is condemned for loss of memory. Forgetfulness of our own sins leads to lack of compassion; remembering how our sins have gone unpunished by God should lead us to forgive others. Through forgetfulness of God's compassion, we can end up becoming cruel to each other. That is why at the beginning of each Eucharist we are invited to be mindful of our own sins. Only when we do that can we pray the "Our Father": "forgive us our trespasses, as we forgive those who trespass against us".

The purpose of calling our sins to mind is not to paralyse us, but to remind us that we all live in the gracious forgiveness of God. To forget that is theological suicide. Whoever we are, we remember our sins because we need to remember always to forgive.

June

Sunday
2
The Most Holy Body & Blood of Christ (Corpus Christi)

Monday
3
9th Week in Ordinary Time
St Charles Lwanga & Companions

Tuesday
4

Wednesday
5

Thursday

6

Friday *The Most Sacred Heart of Jesus*

7

Saturday *The Immaculate Heart of the Blessed Virgin Mary*

8

You wicked slave! I forgave you all that debt because you pleaded with me. Should you not have had mercy on your fellow slave, as I had mercy on you?

Matthew 18:32-33

June

Sunday *10th Sunday in Ordinary Time*

9

Monday

10

Tuesday *St Barnabas, Apostle*

11

Wednesday

12

✝

June

Thursday _St Anthony of Padua_
13

Friday
14

Saturday
15

June

Sunday *11th Sunday in Ordinary Time*
16 *Day for Life (E&W)*

Monday
17

Tuesday
18

Wednesday
19

✝

Thursday
20

Friday
21

Saturday Ss John Fisher & Thomas More (England)
22

June

Sunday *12th Sunday in Ordinary Time*

23

Monday *The Nativity of St John the Baptist*

24

Tuesday

25

Wednesday

26

Thursday Our Lady of Perpetual Help (C.Ss.R.)

27

Friday St Irenaeus

28

Saturday Ss Peter & Paul, Apostles (Ireland)

29

June/July

Sunday
30

Ss Peter & Paul, Apostles (E&W,S)

13th Sunday in Ordinary Time (Ireland)

Monday
1

Tuesday
2

Wednesday
3

St Thomas, Apostle

✝

July

Thursday

4

Friday

5

Saturday

6

✝

The Parable of the Lost Sheep

Luke 15:4-7

*T*he format of Luke's twin parables of the Lost Sheep and the Lost Coin follow the same dramatic action. Of course, this pattern could be interrupted at any moment through lack of interest.

having ·········➤ **losing** ·········➤ **searching** ·········➤ **finding**

restoring with joy ·············➤ **rejoicing in community**

The parable of the Lost Sheep opens in crisis with a shepherd, after counting the sheep, realising that he has lost one of them. Even though the shepherd in the parable has ninety-nine safely at hand, the loss of one sheep still matters to him. He does not write off the missing sheep as a lost cause; he does not sit down in the wilderness and mourn its loss, but goes off in search of the lost one. The loss is registered as important, so the search begins. Search is not automatic after loss; only if the loss is registered as important do we seek out what is lost. As the saying goes, "Where there is no love there is no loss."

The sheep is lost in the middle of the wilderness, not among fenced fields, so the looking has to be serious, over crags and among rocks and crevices, and it continues until the shepherd finds the lost one. When he finds it, the real work begins, for he has to shoulder the weight of the frightened sheep and make his way back through the rocky wilderness to home. But when he lays the weight of the sheep on his shoulders, the shepherd rejoices: his joy is greater than the burden of restoration he has to endure. That joy is intact at journey's end when the shepherd wants to share it with his friends and neighbours.

Sir John Everett Millais, The Lost Sheep, engraving published 1864

Even though the sheep was lost, the shepherd saw the lost one as still belonging to him; that connection was never severed through the sheep's being lost. That the shepherd should go to such trouble to search for one per cent of his property emphasises the depth of feeling impelling him. Given Luke's setting of the parable, the clear inference is that the tax collectors and sinners, despite being lost and despite being rejected by the Pharisees and the scribes, still belong to God, and that God seeks to bring them back safely to the fold. This, for Luke, is what God is seen to be doing through the person of Jesus: "For the Son of Man came to seek out and to save the lost" (Luke 19:10).

July

Sunday *14th Sunday in Ordinary Time*

7

Monday

8

Tuesday *Our Lady of Aberdeen (Scotland)*

9

Wednesday

10

✝

July

Thursday *St Benedict (Europe)*

11

Friday *St John Jones (Wales)*

12

Saturday

13

Just so, I tell you, there will be more joy in heaven over one sinner who repents than over ninety-nine righteous persons who need no repentance.

Luke 15:7

July

Sunday *15th Sunday in Ordinary Time*

14 *Sea Sunday*

Monday St Bonaventure

15

Tuesday *Our Lady of Mount Carmel*

16

Wednesday

17

✝

Thursday
18

Friday
19

Saturday
20

July

Sunday *16th Sunday in Ordinary Time*
21

Monday *St Mary Magdalene*
22

Tuesday *St Bridget (Europe)*
23

Wednesday
24

✝

Thursday St James, Apostle
25

Friday Ss Joachim & Anne
26

Saturday
27

July

Sunday *17th Sunday in Ordinary Time*

28

Monday *Ss Martha, Mary & Lazarus*

29

Tuesday

30

Wednesday *St Ignatius of Loyola*

31

✝

Thursday *St Alphonsus Liguori C.Ss.R.*

1

Friday

2

Saturday

3

The Parable of the Prodigal Son

Luke 15:11-32

*T*he story is told of a father who has two sons and who loses them both. One son is lost in a far country, and the other is lost in the wilderness of his own hostility. One leaves home in the fond hope that he will experience happiness in the unfamiliar, only to discover it is found at the heart of the familiar. One stays at home but is such a stranger to the love and acceptance which surround him that he might as well be an alien in a foreign land. They are a mixed human family in which tenderness and selfishness and hostility vie with each other for possession.

The younger son yearns for a life different from that at home. He leaves home and soon discovers that his promised land is barren. He experiences failure, but his failure is not unimportant: through his failure he comes to himself.

The elder son does not leave home, but staying at home has not led him to hospitality. When he returns from the fields, with the sweat of the slave on his brow, he hears music and dancing. Rather than hurry in to join the party, he reacts with anger. Unlike his father, he does not have the generous instinct to rush to meet the younger brother. The elder brother refuses to move. He sees himself as a slave: "All these years I have slaved for you..." His own anger immobilises him. Now it is he who is far from home. He is "the separated one" who cannot move to accept his brother and rejoice with him.

The father loves both his sons and he lives in the hope that they will love and accept each other. The father's attitude reflects the generosity of Jesus' way of dealing with sinners. Jesus has both

Arcabas, Le Fils Prodigue

sons represented in his audience: the separated ones who, like the elder son, refuse to welcome their brother sinners; and the sinners who, like the younger son, hope to be accepted when they make for home. Jesus' appeal, like the father's appeal, is aimed at religious intolerance.

Like the elder son in the parable, the Pharisees and scribes are good and upright. They do their duty faithfully. They may be without sin. But if their sinlessness adds up to lovelessness, what virtue is in it? If their religious fidelity permits them to reject their brother, what purpose does it serve? They end up being enslaved by their own religious intolerance.

Jesus does not say if the elder brother moves to accept his younger brother who was lost. The story is still being told today. The answer is in our own behaviour.

August

Sunday *18th Sunday in Ordinary Time*
4

Monday *August Bank Holiday (Scotland)*
5

Tuesday *The Transfiguration of the Lord*
6

Wednesday
7

✝

August

Thursday *St Dominic*

8

Friday *St Teresa Benedicta of the Cross (Europe)*

9

Saturday *St Lawrence*

10

Then the father said to him, "Son, you are always with me, and all that is mine is yours. But we had to celebrate and rejoice, because this brother of yours was dead and has come to life; he was lost and has been found."

Luke 15:31-32

August

Sunday
11
19th Sunday in Ordinary Time

Monday
12

Tuesday
13

Wednesday
14
St Maximilian Kolbe

✝

Thursday   *The Assumption of the Blessed Virgin Mary*
15

Friday
16

Saturday
17

August

Sunday *20th Sunday in Ordinary Time*
18

Monday
19

Tuesday *St Bernard*
20

Wednesday *St Pius X*
21

✝

Thursday

22

Friday

23

Saturday *St Bartholomew, Apostle*

24

August

Sunday *21st Sunday in Ordinary Time*
25

Monday *Bank Holiday (E,W&I)*
26

Tuesday *St Monica*
27

Wednesday *St Augustine*
28

Thursday *The Passion of St John the Baptist*
29

Friday
30

Saturday
31

September

Sunday
1
22nd Sunday in Ordinary Time
World Day of Prayer for the Care of Creation

Monday
2

Tuesday
3
St Gregory the Great (England)

Wednesday
4

✝

September

Thursday *St Mother Teresa of Calcutta*

5

Friday

6

Saturday

7

The Parable of the Good Samaritan

Luke 10:25-37

*I*n the parable of the Good Samaritan Jesus faces the old antagonism between his own people and the Samaritans. The Samaritans were despised as the mixed-race descendants of northern Jews who had intermarried with foreign settlers. That racial difference made for religious difference, and when the southern Jews returned from exile in 520 BC they refused to allow the Samaritans to help them rebuild the Temple. In response the Samaritans established their rival priesthood and temple. The breach was soon complete. Each group's loyalty to its own tradition served to nourish its hostility towards the other group.

The Jewish lawyer's question, "Who is my neighbour?" gives Jesus the opportunity to confront this old hostility. For the traditional Jew, a neighbour was someone within the boundaries of your own racial and religious circle.

In the parable Jesus questions his own people's attitude to the Samaritans. When someone says to him, "Yes, but we have our own way of doing things here", Jesus' response is to question that way. The shock to the system is that the hero is a despised Samaritan, the one who is publicly cursed in synagogues; the one whose evidence is not acceptable in a court of law. He is the one Jesus holds up as the neighbour in the kingdom of God. He is the one who went beyond the limits of religion to extend the boundary of compassion.

In the parable Jesus is questioning an attitude that has been taken for granted for hundreds of years, one which is enshrined in tradition and law. And Jesus is challenging the lawyer to be disloyal to that tradition. If your religious tradition invites you to despise other people, then you must be disloyal to your tradition.

September

Vincent van Gogh, The Good Samaritan

If loving your neighbour means being disloyal to your tradition, then disloyalty itself becomes a virtue. The ultimate loyalty is love.

We know from experience the weight of inherited hostility. We know that to help some people is not only an act of love but an act of defiance against the bigotry that tries to pass itself off as religion. Jesus tells us that as his disciples we must be disloyal to those who would educate our hate. If religion needs hate to nurture it, who needs that kind of religion? The Gospel comes to challenge our hate and to promote our love. And that challenge is always to extend the boundaries of our love to include our traditional enemies. If the Gospel does not liberate, then Christ died in vain. He died so that everyone could have life in his name.

September

Sunday *23rd Sunday in Ordinary Time*
8 *Education Day (E&W)*

Monday
9

Tuesday
10

Wednesday *St Deiniol (Wales)*
11

✝

September

Thursday

12

Friday   *St John Chrysostom*

13

Saturday *The Exaltation of the Holy Cross*

14

"Which of these three, do you think,
was a neighbour to the man who fell
into the hands of robbers?" He said,
"The one who showed him mercy." Jesus said
to him, "Go and do likewise."

Luke 10:36-37

September

Sunday *24th Sunday in Ordinary Time*

15 *Evangelii Gaudium Day (E&W)*

Monday *St Ninian (Scotland)*

16 *Ss Cornelius & Cyprian*

Tuesday *St Robert Bellarmine*

17

Wednesday

18

✝

September

Thursday
19

Friday *St Andrew Kim Tae-gon & Companions*
20

Saturday *St Matthew, Apostle & Evangelist*
21

September

Sunday *25th Sunday in Ordinary Time*

22

Monday *St Pius of Pietrelcina*

23

Tuesday

24

Wednesday

25

✝

September

Thursday **Ss Cosmas & Damian**

26

Friday **St Vincent de Paul**

27

Saturday

28

September/October

Sunday *26th Sunday in Ordinary Time*

29

Monday *St Jerome*

30

Tuesday *St Thérèse of Lisieux*

1

Wednesday *The Holy Guardian Angels*

2

✝

Thursday

3

Friday   Harvest Fast Day (E&W)

4   St Francis of Assisi

Saturday

5

✝

The Parable of the Two Sons

Matthew 21:28-32

*J*esus tells the story of a man who has two sons and who asks them both to work in the vineyard. The first son refuses bluntly, "I will not", but afterwards regrets his decision and changes his mind. The second son agrees politely and readily, "I go, sir", but his instant consent is not matched by his behaviour: he doesn't turn up. Jesus' question, "Which of the two did the will of his father?", only allows for one answer. Only one son did anything.

Jesus' own reply identifies the two sons. The son who refused but repented stands for the tax collectors and prostitutes who complied with God's requests set forth in the Baptist's preaching. The other son stands for the priests and scribes who maintain the outward appearance of piety but without any real devotion to the will of God. They did not trust the Baptist, even when they saw the testimony of the changed lives of the tax collectors and prostitutes. Their outward piety, unsupported by obedience to God, is criticised as fake.

The son whose word was "no" but whose action became "yes" is held out to us as the one who did his father's will. The story doesn't tell us why he changed his mind or what the change cost him, only that his generosity of spirit had the last word. In time he caught up with the best that was in him. He was late in doing his father's will, but not too late.

That son had a real counterpart in St Augustine, whose early life was a blunt refusal to follow the Gospel his mother had held out to him. In his *Confessions* he admits his sexual exploits – from the age of seventeen he had a mistress who bore him a son. The

Gospels he regarded as fit only for simple minds; he hunted elsewhere for truth. In time – when he was thirty-two – he caught up with the best in himself and his "no" turned into a committed "yes". The son who eventually said "yes" reflected on his late decision when he wrote:

> Late have I loved thee, O Beauty so ancient and so new, late have I loved thee!... Thou didst call and cry out and burst in upon my deafness; thou didst shine forth and glow and drive away my blindness; thou didst send forth thy fragrance, and I drew in my breath, and now I pant for thee; I have tasted, and now I hunger and thirst; thou didst touch me, and I was inflamed with desire for thy peace.

October

Sunday
6
27th Sunday in Ordinary Time
Day for Life (Ireland)

Monday
7
Our Lady of the Rosary

Tuesday
8

Wednesday
9
St John Henry Newman (England)

✝

October

Thursday
10

Friday
11

Saturday
12

For John came to you in the way of righteousness and you did not believe him, but the tax collectors and the prostitutes believed in him; and even after you saw it, you did not change your minds and believe him.

Matthew 21:32

October

Sunday *28th Sunday in Ordinary Time*

13 *Prisons Week (to 19 October)*

Monday

14

Tuesday *St Teresa of Avila*

15

Wednesday *St Gerard Majella C.Ss.R.*

16

October

Thursday *St Ignatius of Antioch*
17

Friday *St Luke, Evangelist*
18

Saturday
19

October

Sunday
20

29th Sunday in Ordinary Time

World Mission Day

Monday
21

Tuesday
22

Wednesday
23

✝

Thursday
24

Friday Six Welsh Martyrs & their Companions (Wales)
25

Saturday
26

October

Sunday
27
30th Sunday in Ordinary Time
Daylight Savings Time Ends

Monday
28
Ss Simon & Jude, Apostles

Tuesday
29

Wednesday
30

✝

October/November

Thursday
31

Friday *All Saints*
1

Saturday *The Commemoration of All the Faithful Departed (All Souls' Day)*
2

Praying honestly
The Parable of the Pharisee and the Publican

Luke 18:9-14

*I*n the Gospel Jesus addresses people who pride themselves on their virtue while despising everyone else. They honour themselves by humiliating others. His listeners are in for a shock when he tells them the parable of two men who go to the Temple to pray. One was a good man, the other a real crook. One led a decent religious life, the other was mixed up in corruption – tax collectors worked for the Roman occupying power and were experts at lucrative arithmetic. The good and the bad go to pray, but only one of them actually prays.

The Pharisee addresses his prayer to himself. There is no doubt who is in the lead role and his prayer sounds like the annual report of current assets. He blesses God that he is not like so many others, although he seems unsure about who exactly he is. He compares himself to the tax collector. He fasts twice a week and gives ten per cent of his earnings to the poor. But for all his giving, the Pharisee never gives himself. His real self is secret.

The tax collector stands far off in the shadows. He has no annual accounts to boast of: his percentage is stolen from his own people, including poor people. He tells the simple truth about himself: "God, be merciful to me, a sinner!" He knows the truth about who he really is, and he throws himself entirely on God's mercy. He has nothing to offer God but his own wrongdoing and brokenness. They are his. He doesn't go outside himself but recognises his truth and hopes that God's mercy can take care of it. He owns his own sin. His real self is no secret.

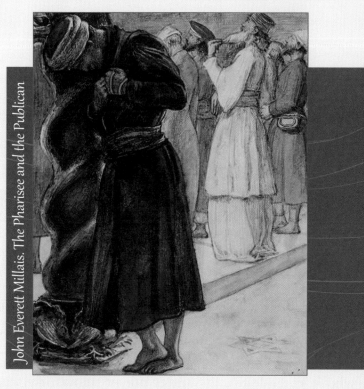

John Everett Millais: The Pharisee and the Publican

Jesus now comments on the story he has told, "I tell you..." Remember who his listeners are – those who honour themselves by despising others. What Jesus now says will come as a shock to their whole religious system. He declares that the tax collector goes home justified while the Pharisee does not. The tax collector gets much more than he asked for: he prayed for mercy but is now justified. In the judgement of Jesus everything is turned upside down. The tax collector's prayer "pierced the clouds". The Pharisee's prayer reached its destination: himself.

If we come to pray and realise that our religion has a heavy investment in despising other people then we will just go home again as we came. "God, be merciful to us, sinners" is the whole truth and nothing but the truth. Anything else is for the mercy of God.

November

Sunday
3
31st Sunday in Ordinary Time

Monday
4
St Charles Borromeo

Tuesday
5

Wednesday
6
All the Saints of Ireland (Ireland)

✝

Thursday

7

Friday *All Saints of Wales (Wales)*

8

Saturday *The Dedication of the Lateran Basilica*

9

For all who exalt themselves will be humbled, but all who humble themselves will be exalted.

Luke 18:14

November

Sunday
10

32nd Sunday in Ordinary Time
Remembrance Day

Monday
11

St Martin of Tours

Tuesday
12

St Josaphat

Wednesday
13

✝

Thursday
14

Friday *St Albert the Great*
15

Saturday *St Margaret (Scotland)*
16

November

Sunday *33rd Sunday in Ordinary Time*
17 *World Day of the Poor*

Monday
18

Tuesday
19

Wednesday
20

✝

November

Thursday
21

Friday *St Cecilia*
22

Saturday *St Columban*
23

November

Sunday *Our Lord Jesus Christ, King of the Universe*
24 Youth Day (E&W)

Monday Last Week in Ordinary Time
25

Tuesday
26

Wednesday
27

✝

November

Thursday
28

Friday
29

Saturday *St Andrew, Apostle*
30

December

Sunday *1st Sunday of Advent*

1

Monday

2

Tuesday *St Francis Xavier*

3

Wednesday

4

✝

December

Thursday
5

Friday *St Nicholas of Myra*
6

Saturday *St Ambrose*
7

✝

The Parable of the Widow and the Unjust Judge

Luke 18:1-8

According to the tradition of Israel a judge was expected to be impartial except to three groups of people – the widow, the orphan and the stranger. Because these people lived in the absence of familiar love and support, they were vulnerable in a society where influence and money talked. A judge was expected to be partial to them and champion their cause to ensure their rights. The religious law stated: "You shall not abuse any widow or orphan. If you do abuse them... I will surely heed their cry" (Exodus 22:23).

When we meet the judge and the widow in the parable we meet them at a crisis point, when both of them are maimed. We have no case history for the widow but we do for the judge. He is a man who is influenced neither by religious principle nor by public opinion. Both justice and compassion are absent from his dealings with the widow. She has no influential friends to bring pressure on the judge and she has no money to bribe him: all she has is the justice of her cause and her own persistence.

The justice of her cause, however, is clearly not enough. She has nerve and she exercises it relentlessly on the judge. He refuses her "for a while" but she refuses for even longer to take him seriously! It becomes a war of nerves and eventually it's his nerves that give in: he grants her justice for the sake of his own health. She puts him on the sick list and he can imagine himself being worried to death. In fact the widow does the judge an enormous favour: she exhausts him into justice. Her persistence pays off in the end.

James Tissot, *The Widow and the Unjust Judge*

In telling the parable Jesus contrasts God with the judge, arguing that if an unjust man can come to justice eventually, how much more will God answer his chosen ones: will he delay long in helping them?

Jesus encourages us to be persistent in our prayer and never lose heart. In an age where we have become accustomed to instant coffee and instant results, we are impatient with what appear to be endless delays. But the values we cherish are not instantly available: values like peace and justice take time to establish. The danger is that we give up too quickly, that we rest our case too easily. We have to be persistent; we have to invest our time in our beliefs. If a sixty-one-year-old bagpiper can still search for a wife, we can still search for justice until the unjust are worried to death.

December

Sunday *2nd Sunday of Advent*

8

Monday

9

Tuesday

10

Wednesday

11

✝

Thursday
12

Friday *St Lucy of Syracuse*
13

Saturday *St John of the Cross*
14

nd will not God grant justice to his chosen
ones who cry to him day and night? Will
he delay long in helping them? I tell you,
he will quickly grant justice to them.

Luke 18:7-8

December

Monday
16

Tuesday
17

Wednesday
18

✝

Thursday

19

Friday

20

Saturday

21

December

Sunday   *4th Sunday of Advent*

22   Expectant Mothers

Monday

23

Tuesday

24

Wednesday   *The Nativity of the Lord*

25

✝

December

Thursday | Boxing Day Bank Holiday

26 | St Stephen, the First Martyr

Friday | St John, Apostle & Evangelist

27

Saturday | The Holy Innocents, Martyrs

28

December / January 2025

Sunday *The Holy Family of Jesus, Mary & Joseph*

29

Monday *New Year Bank Holiday (E&W)*

30

Tuesday *New Year Bank Holiday (Scotland)*

31

Wednesday *Mary, the Holy Mother of God*

1

✝

Thursday Ss Basil & Gregory

2

Friday

3

Saturday The Epiphany of the Lord (Ireland)

4

	January	February	March	April	May	June
Mon						
Tue				1		
Wed	1			2		
Thu	2			3	1	
Fri	3			4	2	
Sat	4	1	1	5	3	
Sun	5	2	2	6	4	1
Mon	6	3	3	7	5	2
Tue	7	4	4	8	6	3
Wed	8	5	5	9	7	4
Thu	9	6	6	10	8	5
Fri	10	7	7	11	9	6
Sat	11	8	8	12	10	7
Sun	12	9	9	13	11	8
Mon	13	10	10	14	12	9
Tue	14	11	11	15	13	10
Wed	15	12	12	16	14	11
Thu	16	13	13	17	15	12
Fri	17	14	14	18	16	13
Sat	18	15	15	19	17	14
Sun	19	16	16	20	18	15
Mon	20	17	17	21	19	16
Tue	21	18	18	22	20	17
Wed	22	19	19	23	21	18
Thu	23	20	20	24	22	19
Fri	24	21	21	25	23	20
Sat	25	22	22	26	24	21
Sun	26	23	23	27	25	22
Mon	27	24	24	28	26	23
Tue	28	25	25	29	27	24
Wed	29	26	26	30	28	25
Thu	30	27	27		29	26
Fri	31	28	28		30	27
Sat			29		31	28
Sun			30			29
Mon			31			30

July	August	September	October	November	December	
		1			1	Mon
1		2			2	Tue
2		3	1		3	Wed
3		4	2		4	Thu
4	1	5	3		5	Fri
5	2	6	4	1	6	Sat
6	3	7	5	2	7	Sun
7	4	8	6	3	8	Mon
8	5	9	7	4	9	Tue
9	6	10	8	5	10	Wed
10	7	11	9	6	11	Thu
11	8	12	10	7	12	Fri
12	9	13	11	8	13	Sat
13	10	14	12	9	14	Sun
14	11	15	13	10	15	Mon
15	12	16	14	11	16	Tue
16	13	17	15	12	17	Wed
17	14	18	16	13	18	Thu
18	15	19	17	14	19	Fri
19	16	20	18	15	20	Sat
20	17	21	19	16	21	Sun
21	18	22	20	17	22	Mon
22	19	23	21	18	23	Tue
23	20	24	22	19	24	Wed
24	21	25	23	20	25	Thu
25	22	26	24	21	26	Fri
26	23	27	25	22	27	Sat
27	24	28	26	23	28	Sun
28	25	29	27	24	29	Mon
29	26	30	28	25	30	Tue
30	27		29	26	31	Wed
31	28		30	27		Thu
	29		31	28		Fri
	30			29		Sat
	31			30		Sun
						Mon

NOTES

NOTES